Kaleidimals

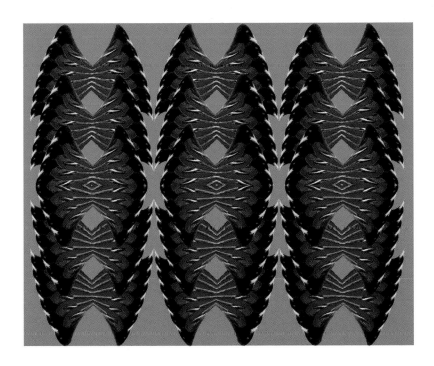

By Marilyn Gaizband

In Partnership With

Audubon Society of Northern Virginia

Dedicated To
My Sister, Dolores Neuman,
Who Gave Me My First Camera

The printing of this book was funded by the Audubon Society of Northern Virginia (ASNV), *www.audubonva.org.* Their mission is to protect birds, other wildlife and their habitats through environmental education, conservation and advocacy. *Proceeds from the sale of this book will go to supporting their mission.*

I would like to thank Diana Bridges, Kevin Munroe, Charlie Willmott and all my friends at Huntley Meadows for their help in compiling this book. I especially want to thank my wonderful husband, Sam Schaen, without whose support I could never have done this.

Much of the information in this book was gathered from the Cornell Lab of Ornithology, National Wildlife Federation and various other Internet sources.

ISBN: 978-0-578-04641-9 Signature Book Printing, www.sbpbooks.com

Kaleidimals

"Kaleidimals" (Kuh-**LYE**-duh-MUHLS) are kaleidoscope-like designs made from photographs of animals. Parts, or sometimes the entire photo of these animals, are arranged repetitively by the artist to create an artistic pattern or image.

In her introductory book featuring birds, the artist presents the original photograph, a guide photo showing what part of the bird is used to build the Kaleidimal, the resulting Kaleidimal, and a collection of fascinating facts about the bird and its habits. With this presentation, readers of all ages can have fun searching for the bird in the Kaleidimal while enhancing their observation skills and learning more about the wonderful world around us. Challenge your sense of adventure by trying to find the bird in the Kaleidimal before using the guide photo to solve the mystery.

Observing wildlife is a lot of fun...something the whole family can enjoy together.

Jeff Shulman

INTERESTING FACTS:

The Pileated Woodpecker was the inspiration for the cartoon character - Woody Woodpecker.

It is an "ecosystem engineer." These woodpeckers forage for their favorite meal, carpenter ants, by digging large, rectangular holes in trees. Other birds as well as mammals are attracted to these large openings and depend on the resulting cavities for survival, feeding on the insects exposed from the excavations.

Pileated woodpeckers do not discriminate between coniferous and deciduous trees—as long as they yield the ants and beetle larvae that make up much of their diet. They sometimes access these morsels by peeling long strips of bark from the tree, but they also forage on the ground and supplement their diet with fruits and nuts.

Unlike many other birds, the pileated woodpecker will move eggs that fall from the nest to another site.

To attract these beautiful birds, put out a suet feeder or leave dead trees and mature woodlands standing.

Pileated Woodpecker

INTERESTING FACTS:

Early in the 19th century egrets were hunted for their feathers which were used in hats. At one point, the plumes were so popular they were worth twice their weight in gold!

Two wealthy Boston women invited all the well dressed ladies of the city to come to tea parties where they made them promise not to wear hats with bird feathers on them. The movement spread from women to men and from state to state. This was the start of a new society. Today the Great Egret is the symbol for the National Audubon Society.

Great Egrets do not eat at night. During the day, they forage alone or in flocks catching fish by standing motionless in the water. They sometimes steal food from smaller birds.

A group of egrets, called a "congregation", "heronry", "skewer", or "wedge" of egrets, depend on clean, pesticide free marshlands with plentiful populations of fish and frogs.

Great Egret

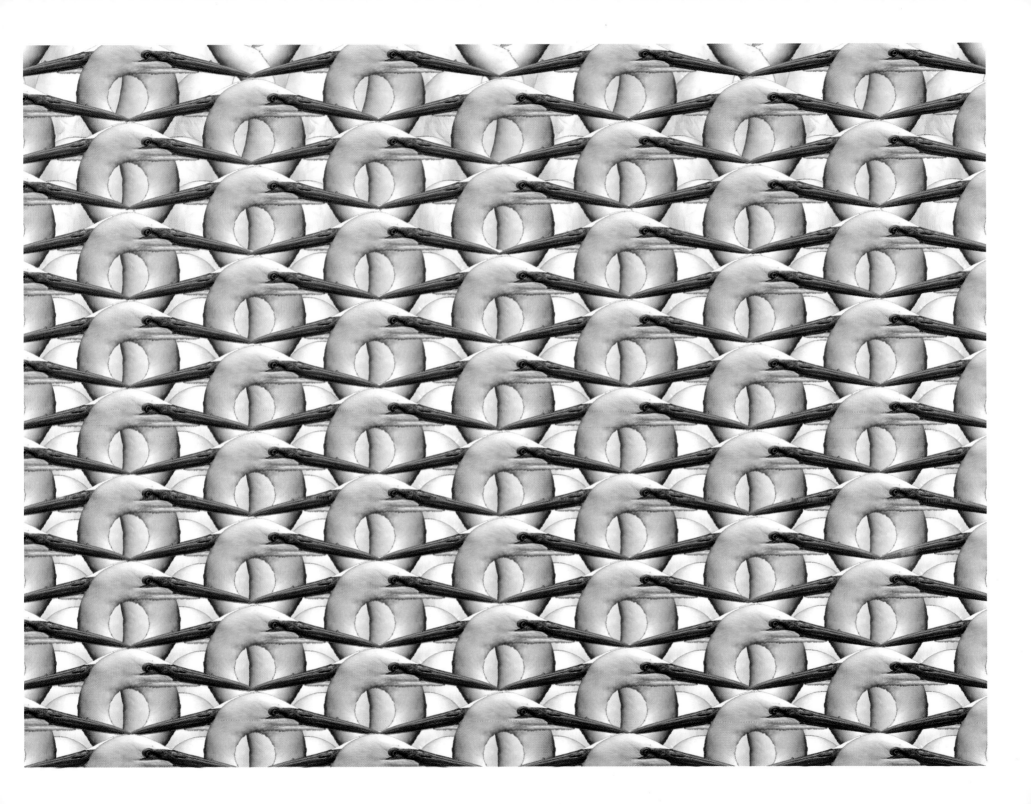

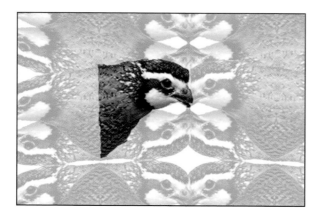

INTERESTING FACTS:

The Northern Bobwhite got its name from its very distinctive call, "bob-white", given by males in mating season.

Northern Bobwhites are attracted to old fields, abandoned farmland and open woodland. They generally live their entire lives within a mile of where they were hatched. If you would like Bobwhites to live near you, plant a meadow of Indian and other native grasses.

Baby Bobwhites are ready to leave the nest as soon as they are born. They are very small and need a lot of bare ground to walk on searching for food. As chicks they eat mostly small bugs. When they get older their diet includes seeds, green plants and other insects.

A group of bobwhites is called a "bevy" or "covey" of Bobwhites.

Northern Bobwhite

INTERESTING FACTS:

Red-breasted Nuthatches have long, strong toes and claws. The hind toe is greatly enlarged, which helps them climb up and down trees. Their short tail aids in their climbing as well.

Red-breasted Nuthatches keep predators and/or competitors from their nests by applying sticky conifer resin to the entrance of its nest hole. The male puts the resin on the outside of the hole while the female puts it around the inside.

Red-breasted Nuthatches mingle with chickadees and kinglets in fall and winter. The alarm call of the chickadees warns them of approaching hawks. Each nuthatch incessantly gives its call, "ank-ank-ank" to enable strays and laggards to keep in touch with the roving band.

A winter suet feeder on a backyard pine tree will be visited often by them. They will use their sharp, solid bill as a hammer to wedge excess food into the bark of the tree.

A group of nuthatches is collectively known as a "jar" of nuthatches.

Red-breasted Nuthatch

INTERESTING FACTS:

The Blue Grosbeak was first described in 1758 by Carolus Linnaeus; a Swedish botanist, physician and zoologist.

They can be found along healthy forest edges of native meadows with little or no pesticides.

Male Blue Grosbeaks get their striking spring plumage from feather wear. While Blue Grosbeaks spend their winter in the South, the brown feather tips rub off leaving the crystal blue plumage by the time they arrive at their breeding grounds.

Blue Grosbeaks sometimes use snakeskin as nesting material, which is thought to thwart predators.

A group of grosbeaks is collectively known as a "gross" of grosbeaks.

Blue Grosbeak

INTERESTING FACTS:

One of the favorite foods of Hairy Woodpeckers is insects. They find the insects by feeling the vibrations the insects make moving about. Hairy Woodpeckers can "hear" the insects under the barks of trees and their long tongues which are covered with sticky substances make the insects easy to catch. They use their chisel-like beaks as a crowbar to remove the bark from the sides of trees and drill for their food.

Another source of food for the Hairy Woodpecker is the Pileated Woodpecker's leftovers. They like to hang out with the larger woodpeckers so they can get anything the Pileateds don't eat.

In addition to insects, Hairy Woodpeckers like to eat spiders, fruits and seeds.

To see Hairy Woodpeckers and other kinds of woodpeckers in your yard, leave dead trees standing and put up a suet feeder.

A group of woodpeckers is called a "descent", "drumming", or "gatling" of woodpeckers.

Hairy Woodpecker

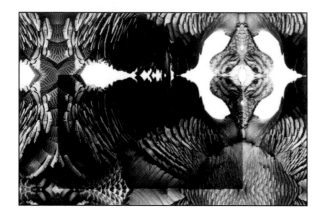

INTERESTING FACTS:

Benjamin Franklin wanted to make the Wild Turkey, rather than the Bald Eagle, the national bird of the United States!

Wild Turkeys have lived in North America almost ten million years.

In England during the 1700s, turkeys were walked to market in herds. They wore booties to protect their feet. They were also walked to market in the United States.

The bare skin on the throat and head of the turkey can change color from flat gray to striking shades of red, white and blue when the bird becomes distressed or excited. Also a spooked turkey can run at speeds up to 20 miles per hour. In addition they can burst into flight approaching speeds between 50-55 mph in a matter of seconds.

Adult turkeys can have 3500 feathers. They live in woods in parts of North America which helps explain their dark feathers. These feathers help them blend in with their woodland homes.

A Wild Turkey has excellent vision and hearing. Its field of vision is about 270 degrees. This is the main reason they continue to elude some hunters.

Wild Turkey

INTERESTING FACTS:

American Goldfinches are sometimes referred to as wild canaries because of their coloring, even though the two birds are not related.

They are the only members of the finch family that shed all of their feathers twice in a single year, including during breeding season. During courtship, one can identify the females by their zigzag flying motion while being chased by males.

Goldfinches weave their nests so tightly that they will temporarily hold water. They can hang upside down to eat, but prefer eating upright.

Goldfinches have an interesting flight call with four syllables that sound like "potato-chip".

You can easily attract these brightly colored birds by hanging a thistle feeder or planting native wildflowers like Purple Coneflower or Evening Primrose.

American Goldfinch

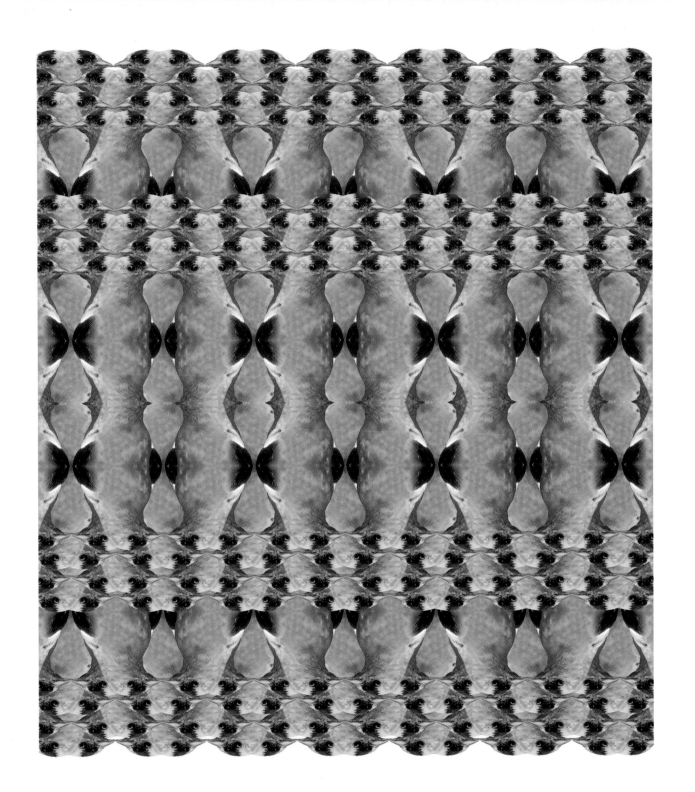

William McHale

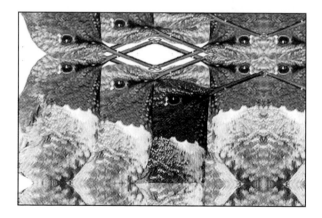

INTERESTING FACTS:

The Ruby-throated Hummingbird is eastern North America's sole breeding hummingbird.

Each day Ruby-throated Hummingbirds consume twice their body weight in food. Nectar drawn from flowers provides only part of the hummingbird's food. Spiders and insects, often seized from the same plants, round out the diet.

In addition, they get food from feeders. Hanging a nectar feeder on your deck in early spring will give you hours of enjoyment all summer. Remember to change the sugar water regularly.

An important pollinator, hummingbirds help plants produce fruit by spreading pollen from flower to flower as they feed.

Amazingly, their tiny 3" bodies fly for hundreds of miles every spring and fall during migration. Their wings beat 55 to 75 times per second. This high-speed flight means that the bird must perch frequently to save energy.

Even though the Ruby-throated Hummingbird has very short legs and cannot walk or hop, it can still scratch its head and neck by raising its foot up and over its wings.

Ruby-throated Hummingbirds have the least number of feathers of any bird. They have a total of 940 feathers.

Ruby-throated Hummingbird

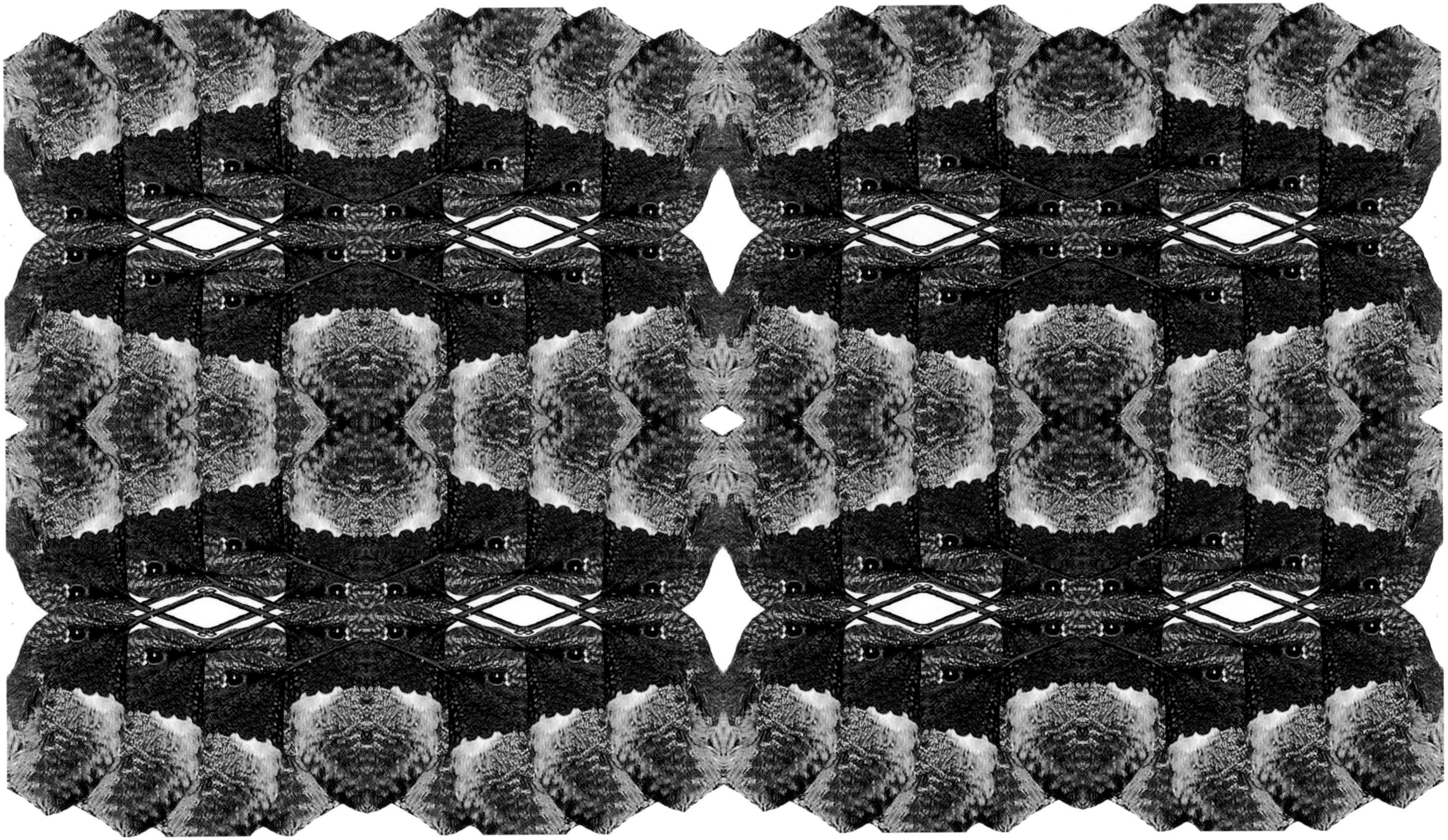

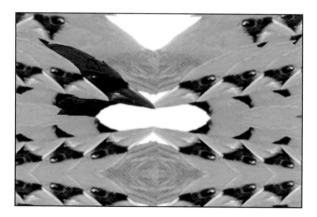

INTERESTING FACTS:

The Northern Cardinal is the state bird of seven states, including Virginia. No other bird holds this distinction.

The male Northern Cardinal may be responsible for getting more people to open a field guide than any other bird.

They are not migratory birds. They tend to remain in one area year long, often throughout their whole lives.

The male cardinal fiercely defends its breeding territory from other males. This is why when a male sees its reflection in a glass surface, it frequently will spend hours fighting the imaginary intruder.

Both male and female cardinals sing but the female normally sings a longer, more complex melody. Singing from the nests is usually a sign to the male that she needs food.

Cardinals love sunflower feeders in the winter. They also love to bathe and drink in ice-free bird baths.

The Northern Cardinal can live up to 15 years in the wild.

Northern Cardinal

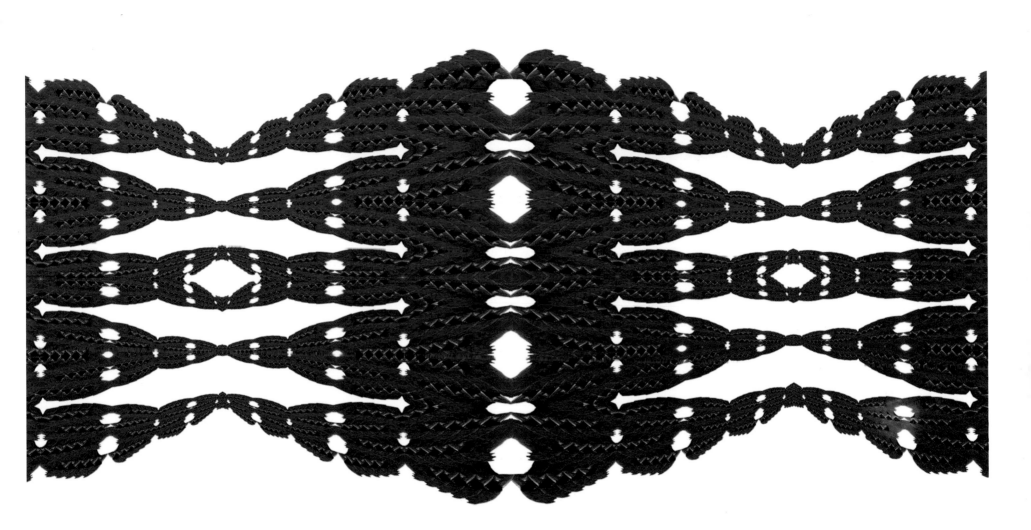

INTERESTING FACTS:

Great Blue Herons are the largest herons in North America.

In the nineteenth century, herons were hunted for their plumes. These beautiful feathers, like those from egrets, were popular decorations for women's hats. Some heron species were severely depleted by hunting, which was outlawed in the early twentieth century.

Great Blue Herons mostly like to eat fish. However, they also eat other small animals. In fact, they have been known to choke to death on prey that was too large. If you have a pond or lakes, let the edges vegetate naturally to attract these gentle giants.

Adult Great Blue Herons have no natural predators, although bobcats and coyotes occasionally kill one that is feeding on the ground.

A group of herons is called a "colony", "battery", "hedge", "pose", "rookery", or "scattering" of herons.

Great Blue Heron

Sam Schaen

INTERESTING FACTS:

The Wood Duck is a distinctively North American species. Fossil remains have been found in widely scattered locations but only in the eastern part of the continent.

It was hunted nearly to extinction during the late 19th and early 20th centuries. Protecting swampy wetlands, leaving dead trees standing and putting up Wood Duck boxes help grow their population. With successful management procedures such as these, there are now well over a million Wood Ducks in North America.

The colorful Wood Duck is one of the only North American ducks that nest in trees. Their young leave the nest soon after hatching. They jump from the nesting cavity, often high up in a tree, to the ground or water.

A group of Wood Ducks is called a "brace", "flush", "paddling", "raft", or "team" of ducks.

Wood Duck

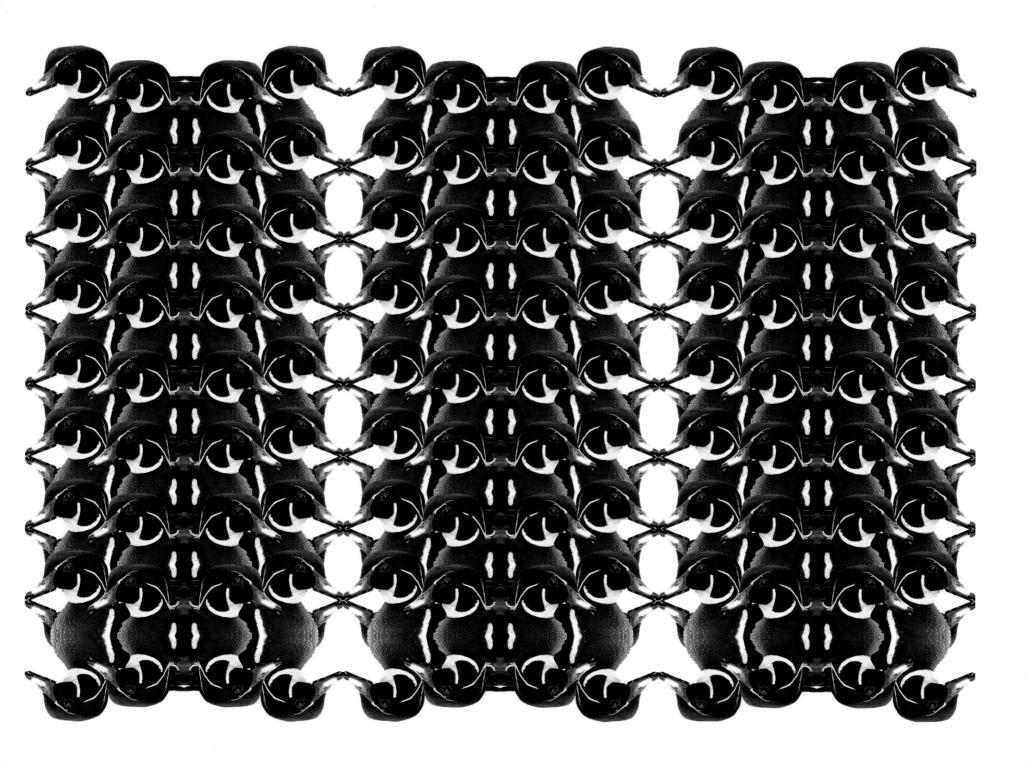

Although the Bald Eagle is our national symbol, some felt it was not the best choice. Benjamin Franklin wrote,

"I wish that the bald eagle had not been chosen as the representative of our country, he is a bird of bad moral character, he does not get his living honestly, you may have seen him perched on some dead tree, where, too lazy to fish for himself, he watches the labor of the fishing-hawk, and when that diligent bird has at length taken a fish, and is bearing it to its nest for the support of his mate and young ones, the bald eagle pursues him and takes it from him... Besides he is a rank coward; the little kingbird, not bigger than a sparrow attacks him boldly and drives him out of the district. He is therefore by no means a proper emblem for the brave and honest... of America.... For a truth, the turkey is in comparison a much more respectable bird, and withal a true original native of America...a bird of courage, and would not hesitate to attack a grenadier of the British guards, who should presume to invade his farmyard with a red coat on."

A pair of Bald Eagles from Florida is credited with building the largest nest measuring 20 feet deep, 13 feet wide and weighing nearly 6000 pounds.

Bald Eagle

INTERESTING FACTS:

The Baltimore Oriole received its name from the fact that the male's colors resembled those on the coat of arms of Lord Baltimore.

Northerners love the Baltimore Oriole since its arrival signals the coming of spring.

Though Baltimore Orioles seem to be good natured, they can be fierce. They use their sharp beaks as weapons and engage their enemies even in mid-air.

Orioles build unusual hanging nests by weaving hair, grass and even string into a small pouch. If you leave yarn and pet hair outside in the spring, a nesting pair could build nearby.

The Baltimore Oriole is the state bird of Maryland. The Baltimore Orioles, an American League baseball team in Baltimore, Maryland, was named after this bird.

A group of orioles is collectively known as a "pitch" or "split" of orioles.

Baltimore Oriole

INTERESTING FACTS:

Ospreys generally pair for life, but if mating is unsuccessful, they will sometimes "divorce".

A female will choose her mate based on the quality and location of the male's nest. Look for these nests on platforms, on top of utility towers and specially erected poles along coastal salt-water areas.

Some Osprey nests can weigh over 1,000 pounds. There is a report of a nest that was used for 125 years and reached a height of 10 feet.

A Beanie Baby, an arrow, a small ax, a rubber boot, a toy sailboat, a pair of pants and a straw hat along with books and boat rudders have all been spotted in Osprey nests along with the usual sticks and native grasses.

Ospreys have an opposable toe that can face forward or backward. While the bird is perched, it usually has three toes in front and one in back. When an Osprey catches a fish, its feet and toes are positioned with two toes on either side of the fish, one foot ahead of the other. The head of the fish faces forward in a streamlined position for transport through the air.

Osprey

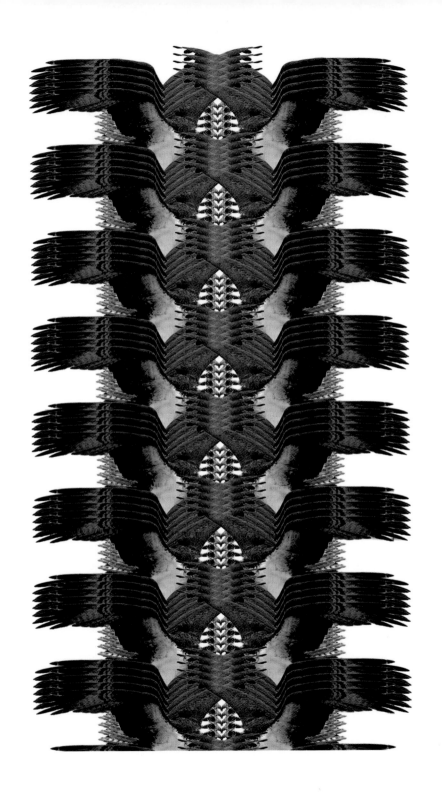

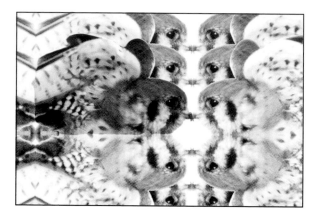

INTERESTING FACTS:

In addition to being the smallest, the American Kestrel is perhaps the most colorful raptor in the world. In addition, it is the most common falcon in North America. It is found from Alaska to Tierra del Fuego, and in farmlands as well as prairies and open fields.

In winter in many southern parts of the range, female kestrels, arriving first, establish their territories in more open habitat, forcing later arriving males into areas with more trees. Farmers can attract these graceful fliers by putting up Kestrel boxes in their fields and reducing pesticide use.

Nestling kestrels back up, raise their tails, and squirt feces onto the walls of the nest cavity. The feces dry on the cavity walls and stay off the nestlings. The nest gets to be a smelly place, with feces on the walls and uneaten parts of small animals on the floor.

There is a color difference between the sexes. The male kestrel has blue on its wings, while the female is mostly brown.

A group of kestrels are collectively known as a " flight", " hover", and "soar" of kestrels.

American Kestrel

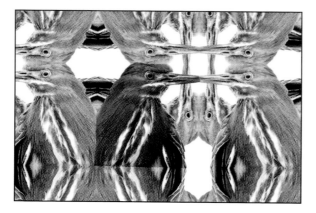

INTERESTING FACTS:

The Green Heron is one of the few tool-using birds. It commonly drops bait onto the surface of the water and grabs the small fish that are attracted. It uses a variety of baits and lures, including crusts of bread, insects, earthworms, twigs, or feathers.

As is typical for many herons, the Green Heron tends to wander after the breeding season is over. Most wanderers probably seek more favorable foraging areas and do not travel far, but occasionally some travel greater distances, with individuals turning up as far away as England and France.

A group of Green Herons is called a "battery", "hedge", "pose", "rookery", or "scattering" of herons.

Green Heron

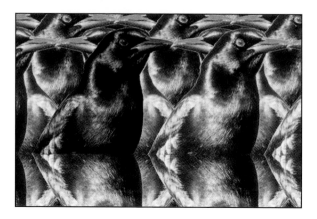

INTERESTING FACTS:

Common Grackles actually walk instead of hop.

Their diet includes insects, the eggs and young of other birds and grains, seeds, fruit and human garbage. In coastal areas they forage at the tide line for small invertebrates, even wading into the water to capture live fish.

Large roving flocks of grackles help disperse seeds and control insect populations.

You might see a Common Grackle hunched over on the ground, wings spread, letting ants crawl over its body and feathers. This is called anting, and grackles are frequent practitioners among the many bird species that do it. The ants secrete formic acid, the chemical in their stings, and this may rid the bird of parasites. In addition to ants, grackles have been seen using walnut juice, lemons and limes, marigold blossoms, chokecherries, and mothballs in a similar fashion.

Common Grackle

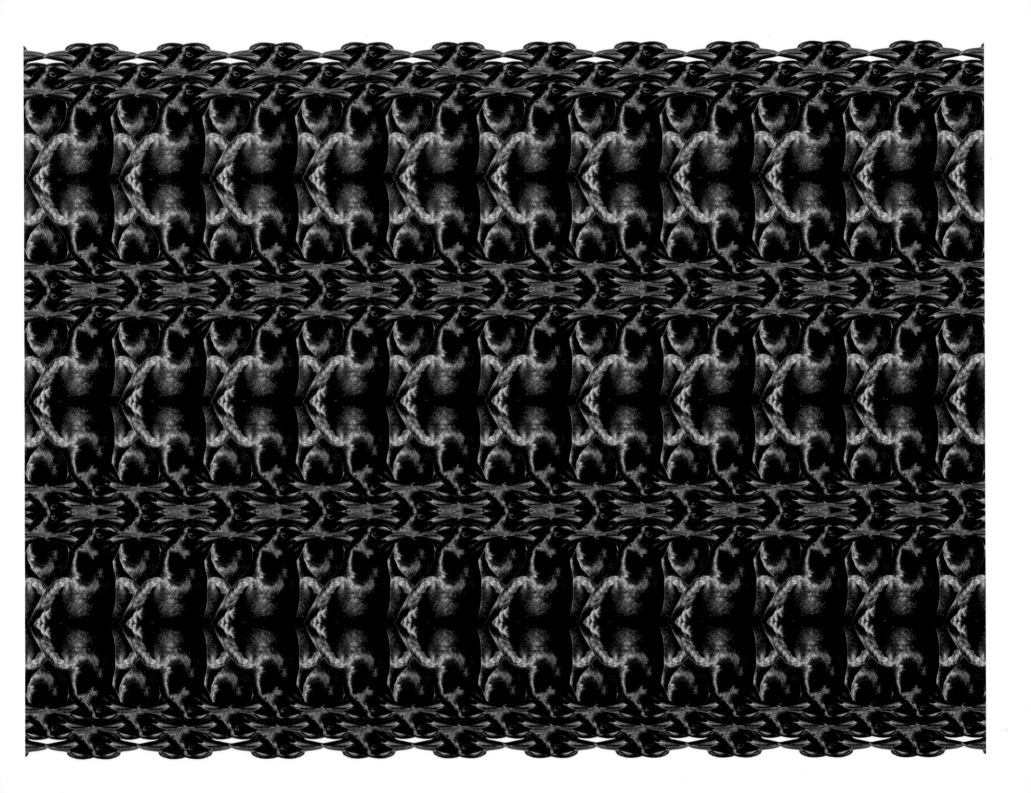

INTERESTING FACTS:

The Black-crowned Night Heron is the most widespread heron in the world. It has a range spanning five continents, including most of North America.

It is a patient hunter and will often stand still and just wait for a frog or other small animal to pass by. It may also hunt by vibrating its bill in the water to lure prey into investigating the disturbance.

Black-crowned Night Herons usually nest in colonies. The breeding colony of wild Night Herons at the National Zoo in Washington, DC, contains more than 200 pairs, with most of the birds arriving from their wintering grounds en masse around March 1.

The adults of the species do not distinguish between their chicks and the chicks of other nests. They will brood chicks which are not their own.

Black-crowned Night Heron

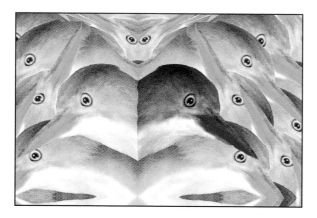

INTERESTING FACTS:

Least Bittern have a habit of straddling reeds in the water which allows it to feed in water that would be too deep for the wading method of other herons.

When alarmed, it freezes in place with its bill pointed up, turns its front and both eyes toward the source of alarm, and sometimes sways to resemble wind-blown marsh vegetation.

A group of bitterns has many collective nouns, including a "dash", "freeze", "pint", "pretense", or "siege" of bitterns.

Least Bittern

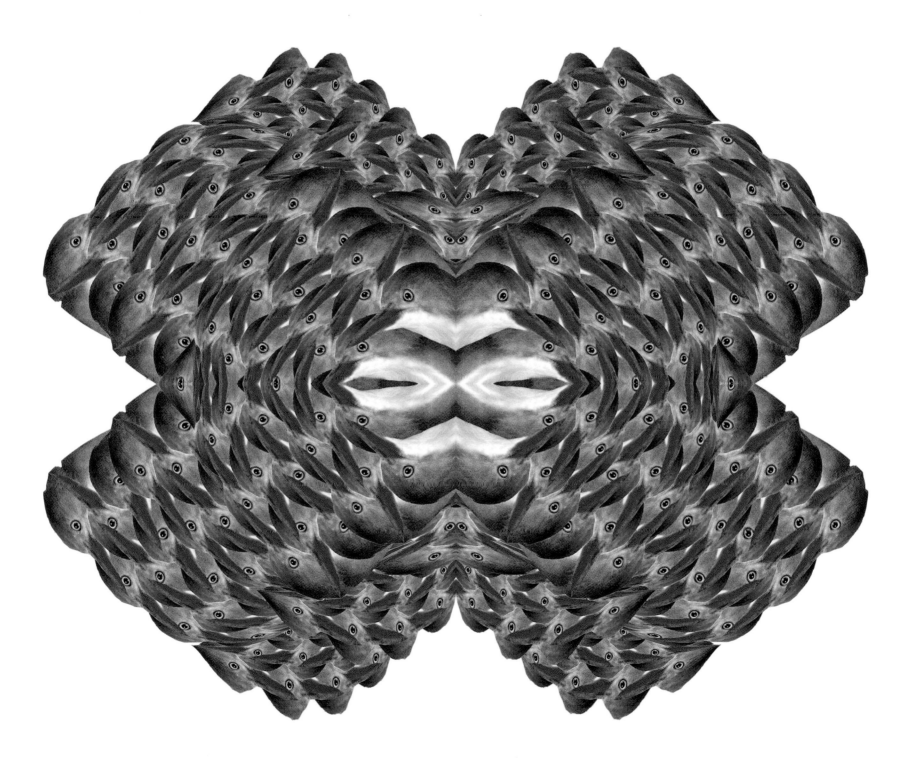

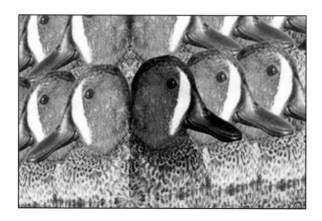

INTERESTING FACTS:

The Blue-winged Teal is among the latest ducks to migrate northward in the spring, and one of the first to migrate southward in the fall. Since they are one of the first ducks to migrate, they are also one of the first to be spotted by fall birdwatchers.

The Blue-winged Teal migrates over long distances. One individual that was banded in Alberta was shot in Venezuela a month later.

It is a sociable duck, often going from group to group within the same species, except during the breeding season.

The Blue-winged Teal has an erratic flight pattern that consists of quick turns and twists, all done in unison with other ducks in the flock.

Blue-winged Teal

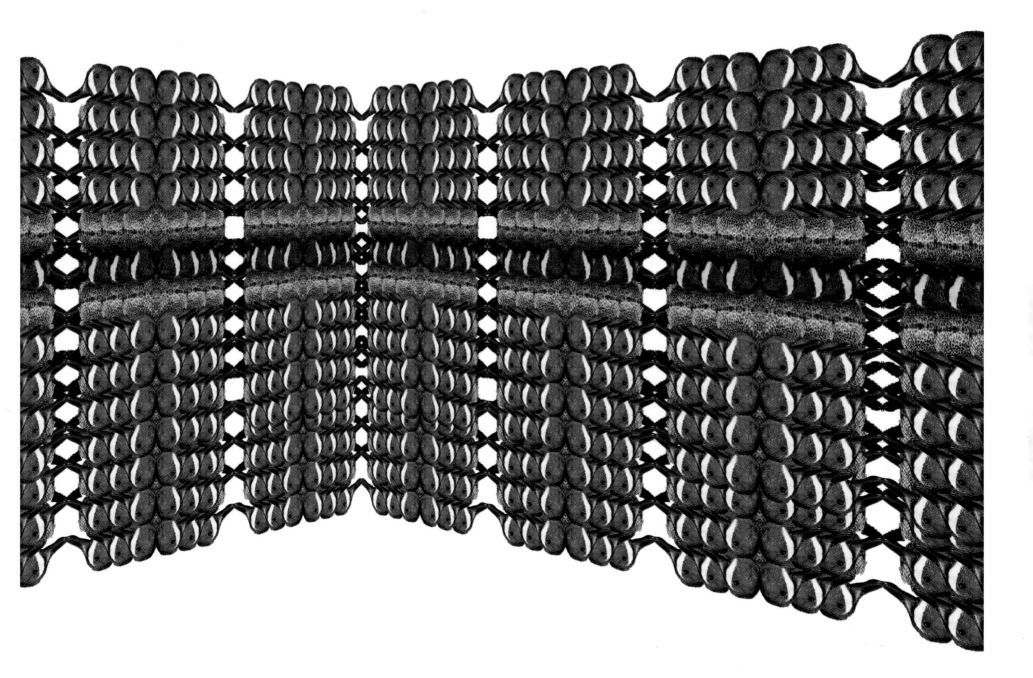

INTERESTING FACTS:

Red-winged Blackbirds change their diets with the season. During the breeding season they eat mostly insects providing valuable insect control. As the babies fledge, the birds switch to eating more and more seeds, and can become problems for farmers. During winter, they eat almost entirely seeds. As they switch, the size of their muscular stomach (their gizzard), switches too, getting bigger and thicker to grind seeds in late summer, and shrinking as they eat more insects in spring. Over the course of a year, their diet is about 75% plant and 25% animal.

Each pair of Red-winged Blackbirds raises 2-3 broods per season. They build a new nest for each brood to protect the babies from becoming infected with parasites that could kill them.

In the summer look for the Red-winged Blackbirds in stands of cattails, Wool and Indian Grass.

During migration the Red-winged Blackbird can travel at over 30 mph.

A group of blackbirds is called a "cloud", "cluster", or "merl" of blackbirds.

Red-Winged Blackbird